Dear Parent,

At Scholastic, we believe it is never too early to begin the learning journey—especially when that journey includes fun, skill-building activities.

To help your child make the most of this workbook, try these helpful hints:

- Choose a **cozy place to work** that is free of distractions. Be sure to have **pencils and crayons** on hand.

- Enjoy **frequent learning sessions**, but keep them short. **Ten to 15 minutes** is an ideal length for most young learners.

- **Praise your child's successes** and encourage his or her efforts. Stickers are a great way to say, **"Job well done!"**

- If your child begins to feel frustrated, **take a break**. You can **revisit the activity** another time.

Let's get started on this first step to helping your child become a confident, lifelong learner.

—The Editors

Trace and write each number.

  1

2

  3

4

5

Trace and write each number.

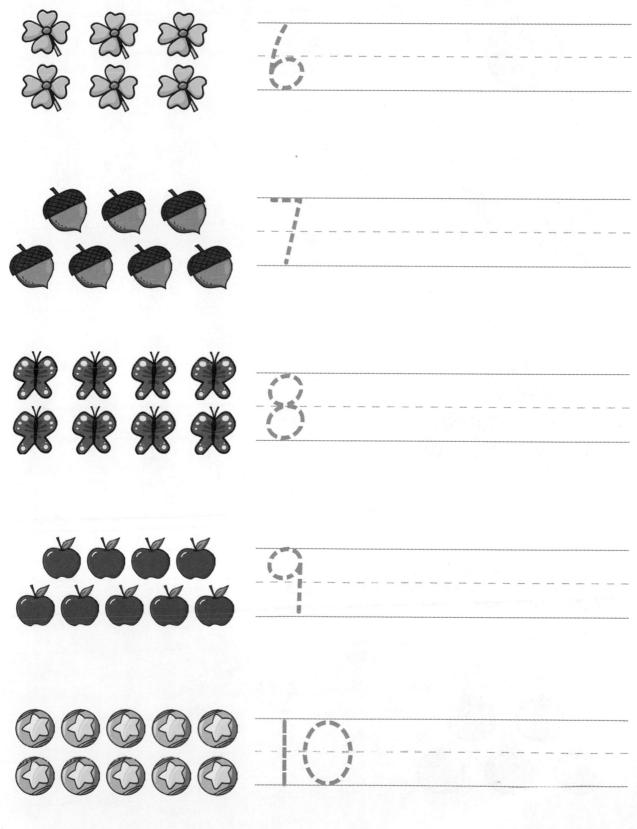

Trace and write each number word.

one

two

three

four

five

Trace and write each number word.

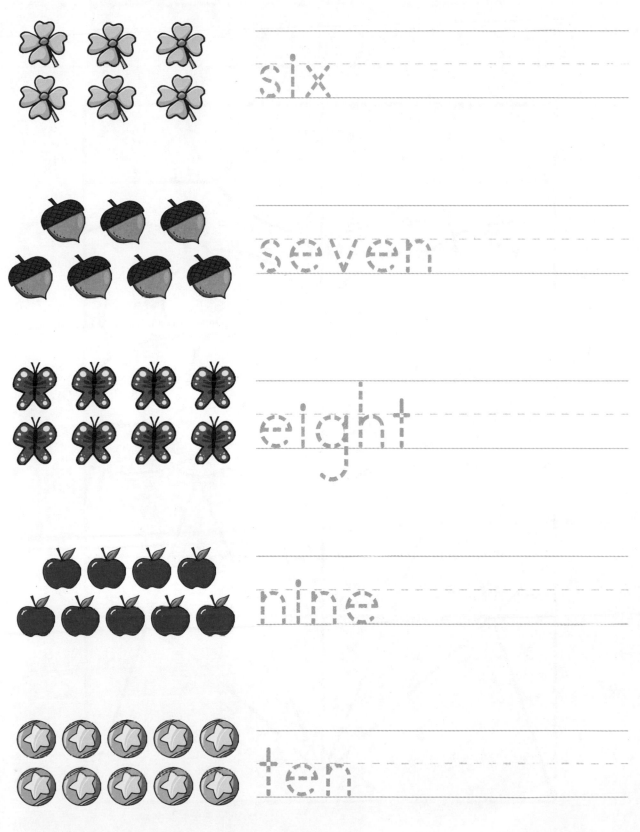

six

seven

eight

nine

ten

Color the picture. Use the color key.

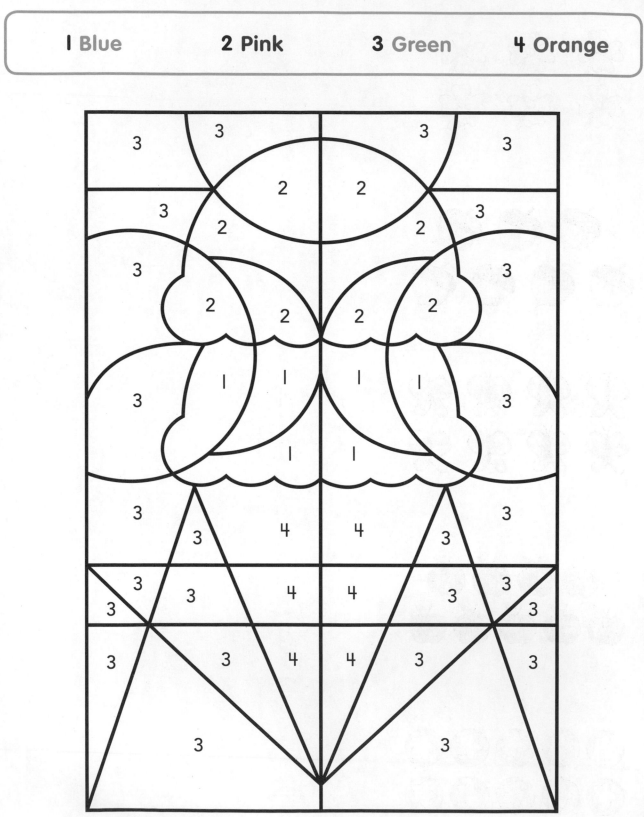

Match each group with the same number of items.

Write the missing number.

1, 2, _____, 4

Count the objects in each box. Circle the number.

| 3 | 2 | 1 | 4 | 1 | 3 | 2 | 3 | 4 |

Draw 3 spots on the dog.

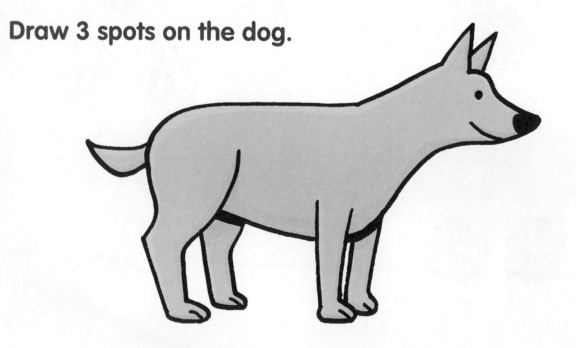

In each row, circle the set that has more.

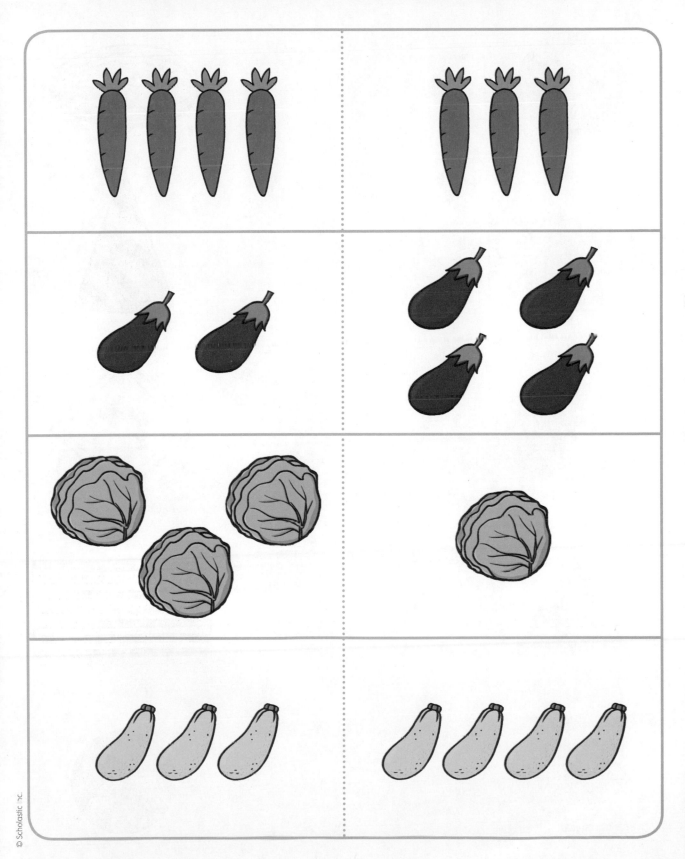

Match the shapes.

Count the frogs on each lily pad. Circle the number.

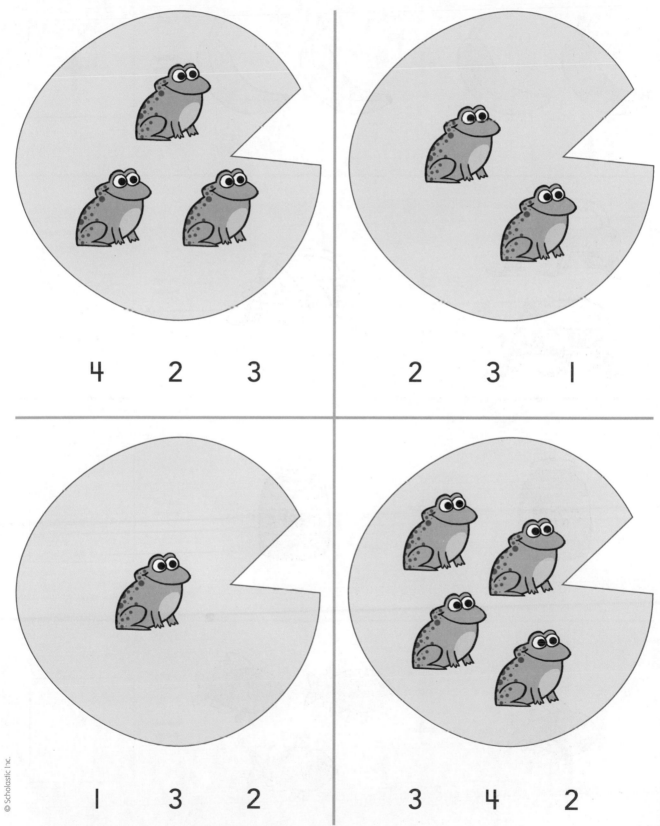

4   2   3   2   3   1

1   3   2   3   4   2

Count. Write the number. The first one is done for you.

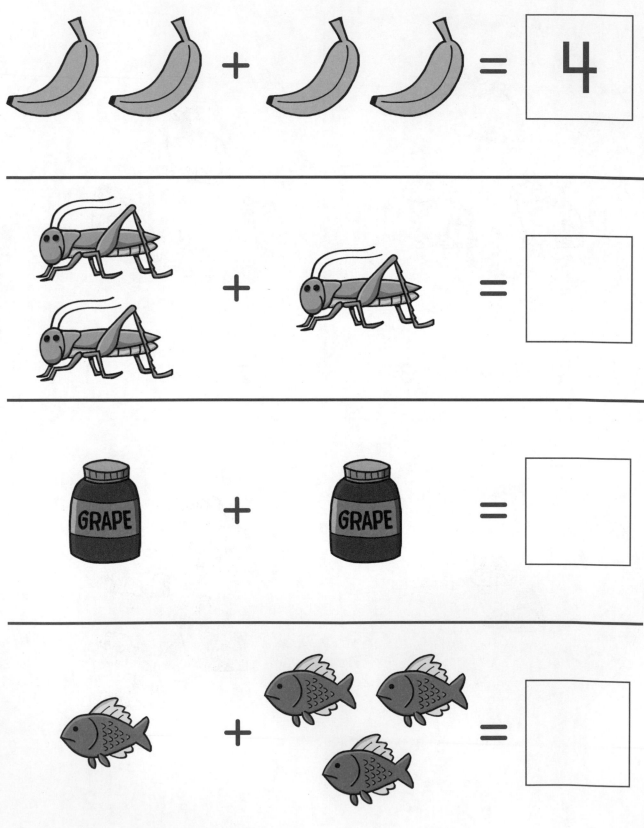

Color the picture. Use the color key.

1 Black **2 Blue** **3 Red** **4 Green** **5 Orange**

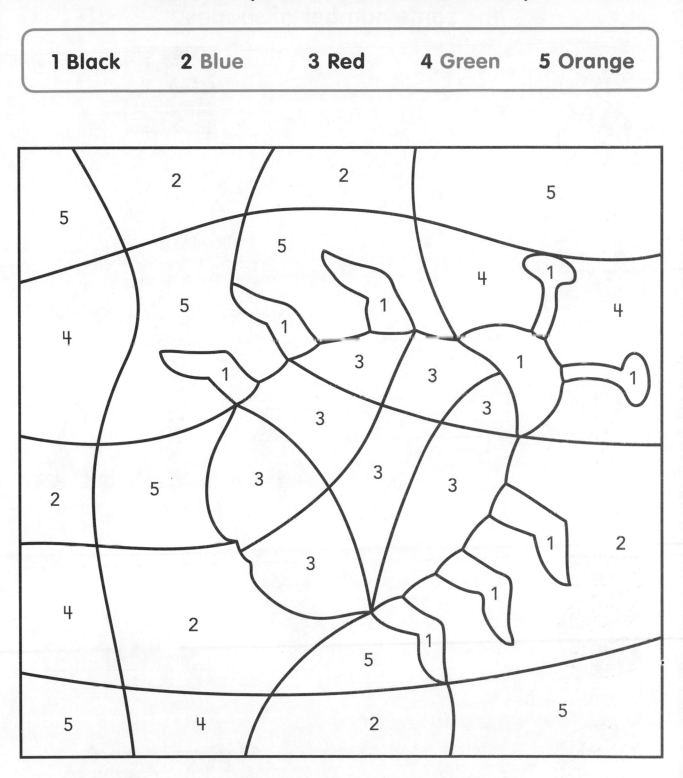

Match each numeral to a set with the same number of shapes.

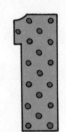 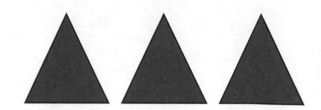

 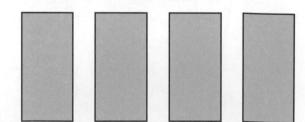

Write the missing number.

2, 3, 4, _____

Count the objects in each box. Circle the number.

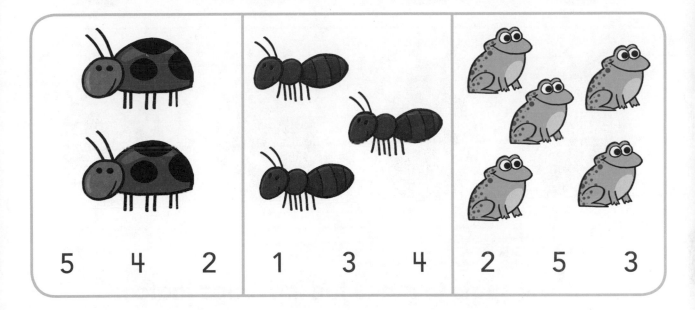

| 5 | 4 | 2 | 1 | 3 | 4 | 2 | 5 | 3 |

Draw 5 bees around this flower.

For each pair, circle the ladybug with fewer spots.

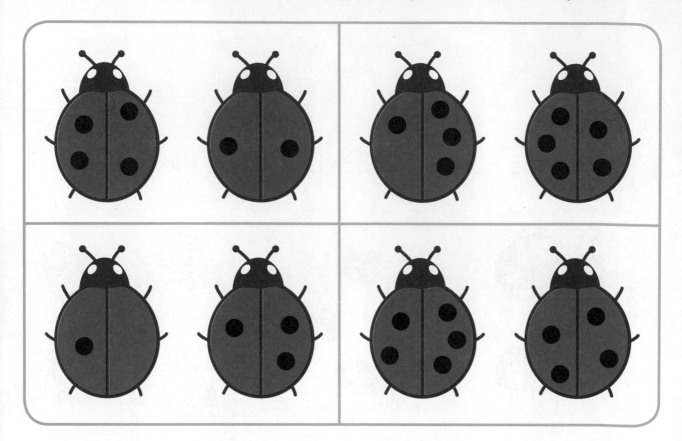

Draw spots to make the ladybugs match.

Count the flowers in each vase. Circle the number.

3   4   2   6   3   4

6   4   8   7   3   5

Count. Then, cross out 1 object in each row.
How many are left? Write the number.
The first one is done for you.

= 2

=

=

=

Color the picture. Use the color key.

1 Red	**2** Orange	**3** Yellow	**4** Green
5 Blue	**6** White	**7** Purple	**8** Brown

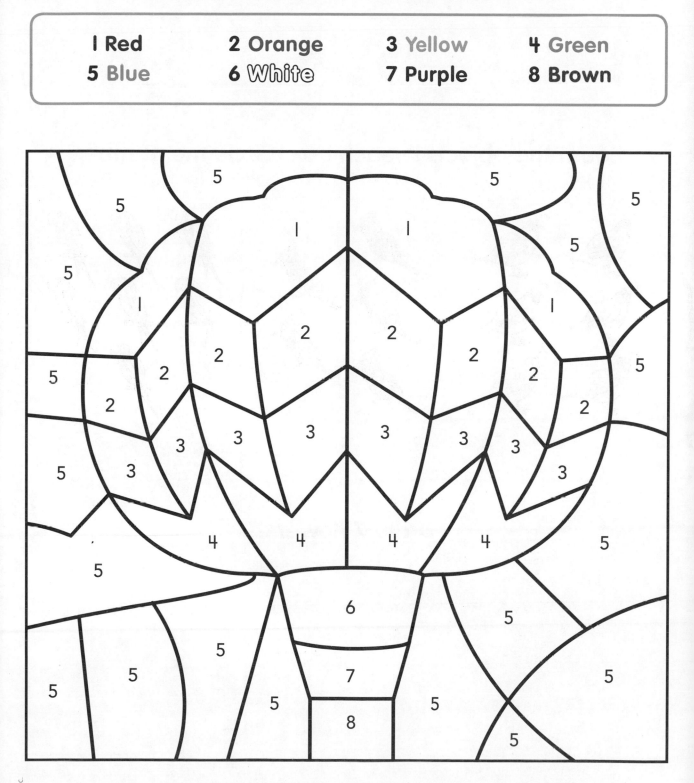

19

Write the missing number.

4, 5, 6, _____

Count the objects in each box. Circle the number.

5   8   6   7   5   6   6   7   8

Draw 7 flowers.

In each row, circle the set that has more.

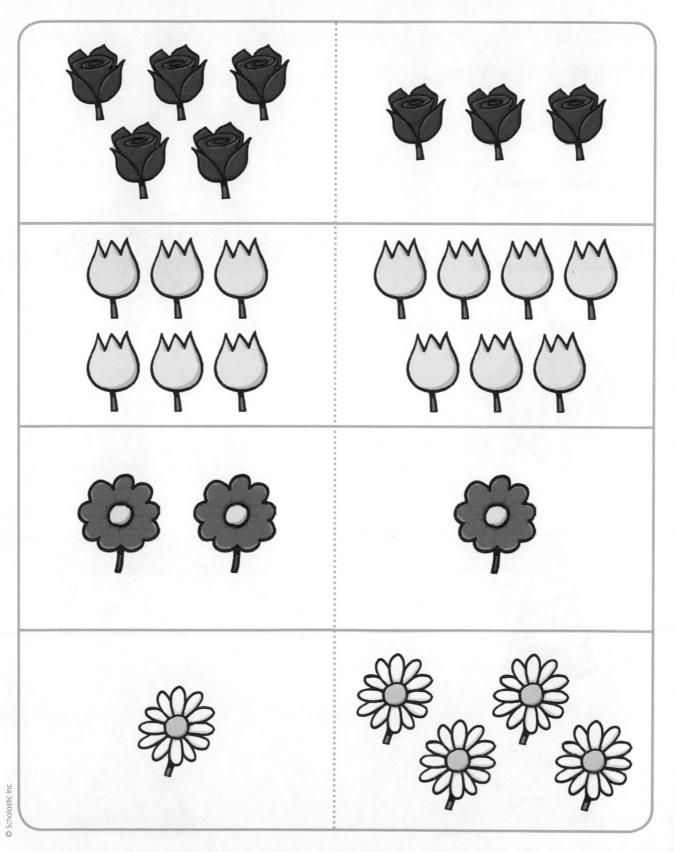

Match the shapes.

Count. Write the number. The first one is done for you.

Match each numeral to a set with the same number of balloons.

Write the missing number.

5, 6, _____, 8

Count the objects in each box. Circle the number.

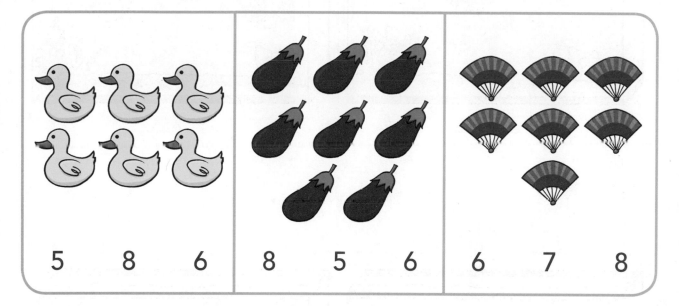

| 5 | 8 | 6 | | 8 | 5 | 6 | | 6 | 7 | 8 |

Draw 8 cookies in the cookie jar.

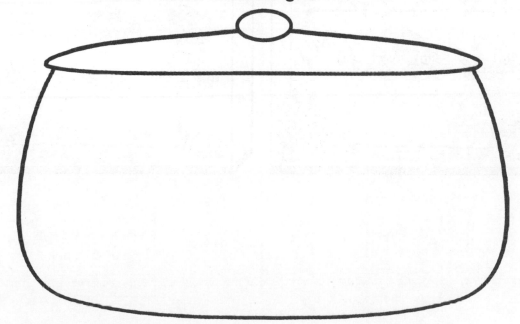

Count the fish in each tank. Write the number.

Count. Then, cross out 2 objects in each row.
How many are left? Write the number.
The first one is done for you.

 =

 =

 =

 =

Color the picture. Use the color key.

1 Red	2 Pink	3 Orange	4 Yellow	5 Green
6 Blue	7 Purple	8 Brown	9 Gray	10 White

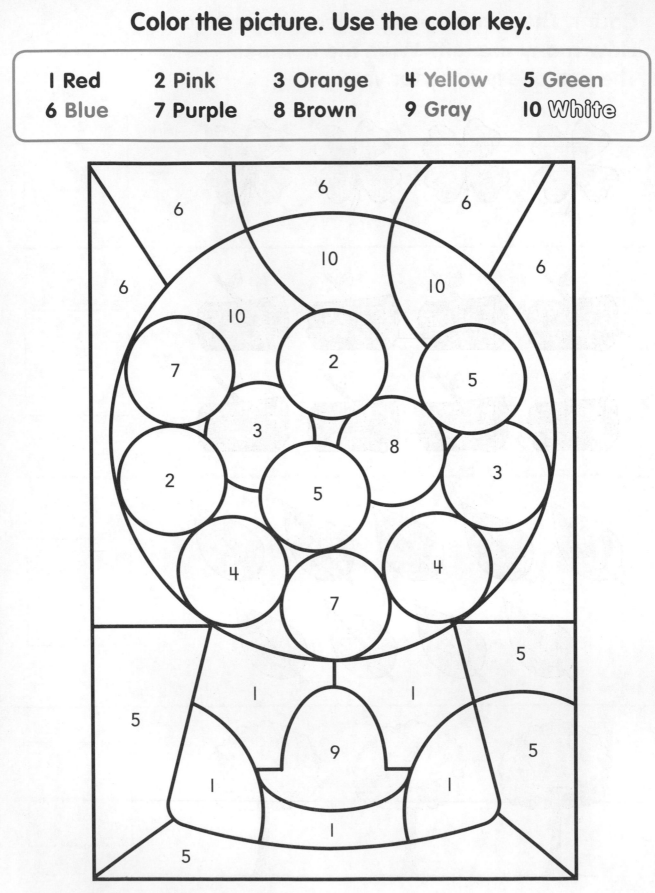

Write the missing numbers.

1, 2, _____, 4, 5, _____, 7, 8, _____, 10

Count the objects in each box. Circle the number.

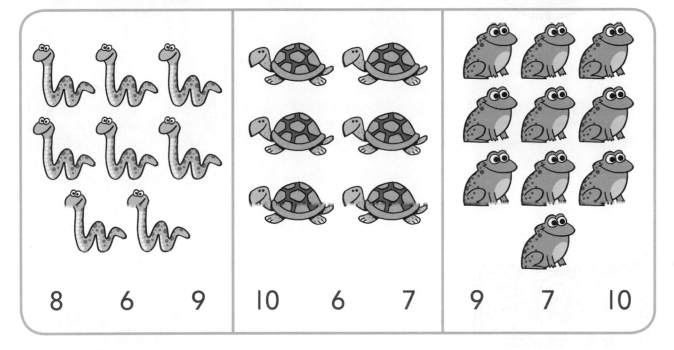

8 6 9	10 6 7	9 7 10

Draw 10 fish.

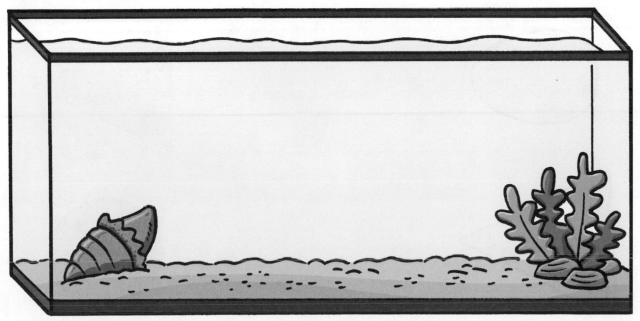

29

Match the shapes.

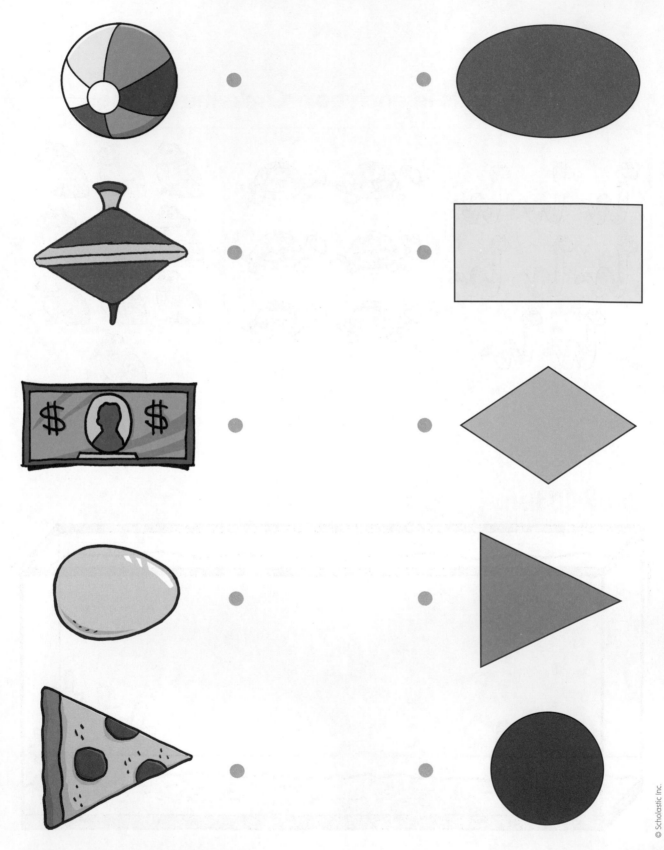

Count the cupcakes. Write the number.

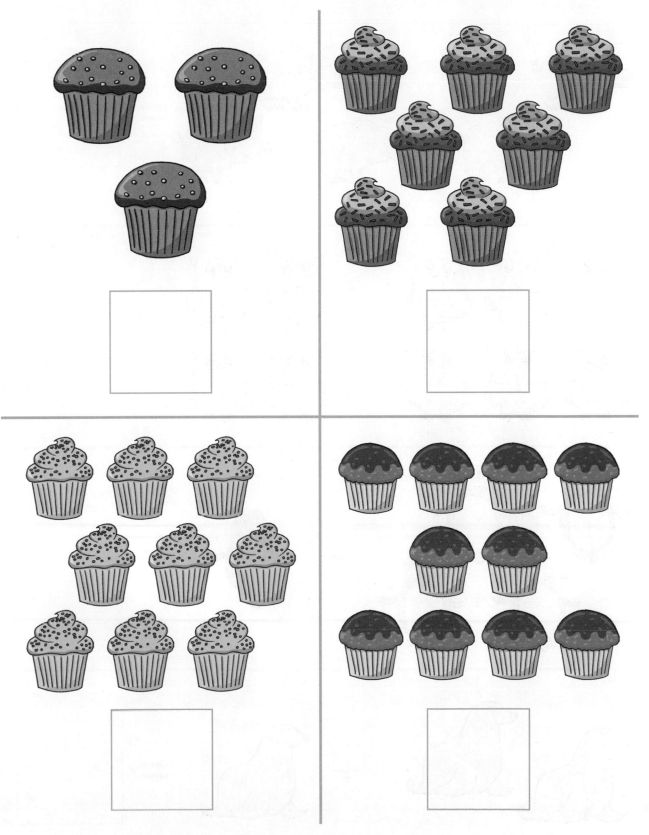

Count. Write the number. The first one is done for you.

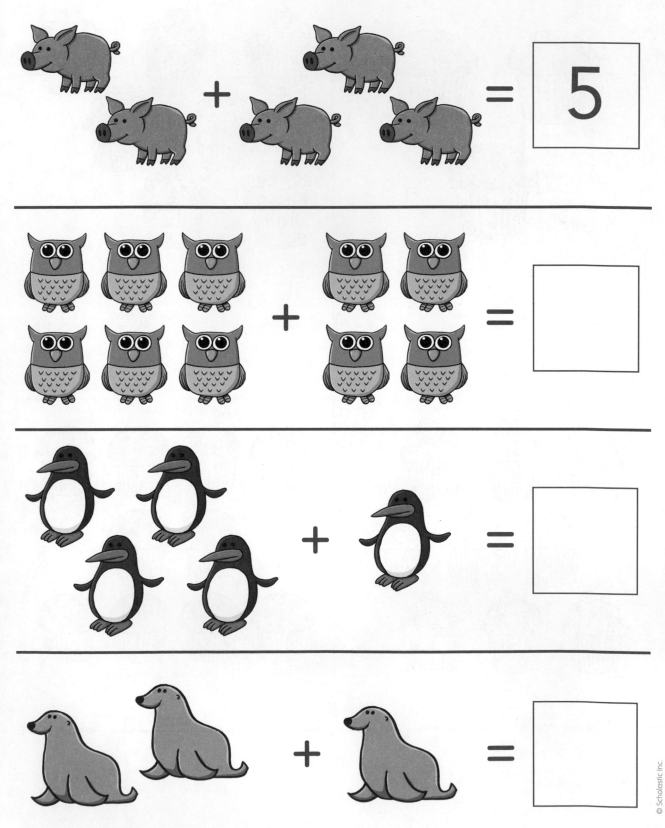